Growth and Changes in Animals: Table of Contents

Y0-BXW-130

GeoWat innovative teacher publishing inc. © 2002

Curriculum Expectations Overview

Curriculum expectations overlap throughout this unit. The teacher may wish to seek out other expectations covered by each lesson.

Understanding Basic Concepts	Lesson
- identify and describe the major physical characteristics of different types of animals;	▪ All About Mammals ▪ All About Reptiles ▪ All About Amphibians ▪ Incredible Insects ▪ The Canada Goose ▪ The Moose
- identify and describe behavioural characteristics that enable animals to survive;	▪ Migration, Hibernation and Dormancy ▪ The Canada Goose ▪ The Moose
- classify a variety of animals using observable characteristics;	▪ Whales ▪ Reptiles: King Cobra
- describe ways in which animals eat their food, move and use their environment to meet their needs;	▪ The Canada Goose ▪ The Moose
- describe changes in the appearance and activity of an animal as it goes through its complete life cycle;	▪ Life Cycle of a Frog ▪ Life Cycle of a Monarch Butterfly
- identify constant traits and changing traits in animals as they grow and compare the appearance of young and mature animals of the same species;	▪ What Will I Look Like When I Grow Up?
- describe ways in which animals respond and adapt to their environment;	▪ How Animals Change With The Seasons ▪ The Canada Goose ▪ The Moose
- compare ways in which different animals care for their young;	▪ Grizzly Bears ▪ Alligator Babies

Curriculum Expectations Overview

Developing Skills of Inquiry, Design, and Communication	Culminating Project
- ask questions about and identify some needs of different animals with which they are familiar and explore possible answers to these questions and ways of meeting these needs;	▪ Step One (pre-writing) "Planning Project"
- plan investigations to answer some of these questions or to find ways of meeting these needs, and describing the steps involved;	▪ Step Two (drafting) "Gathering and Organizing Your Information" ▪ Step Three (revising) "Making It Better"
- use appropriate vocabulary in describing their investigations, explorations, and observations;	▪ Step Six (presenting) "Telling About It"
- record relevant observations, findings, and measurements using written language, drawings and concrete materials;	▪ Step Five (publishing) "Putting It All Together"
- communicate the procedures and results of investigations for specific purposes using drawings, demonstrations and oral and written descriptions;	▪ Finished Product "How To Make A Diorama" "How To Make A Presentation Board"

Curriculum Expectations Overview

Relating Science and Technology to the World Outside the School	Lesson
- describe features of the environment that support the growth of familiar animals;	▪ Home Pet Study
- identify and compare the effects of the seasons on animals;	▪ How Animals Change With The Seasons
- describe ways in which humans can help or harm other living things;	▪ Endangered Species
- demonstrate an understanding of the requirements of small animals for survival;	▪ Home Pet Study
- describe the life processes of an animal that they have observed;	▪ Home Pet Study
- demonstrate an awareness of ways of caring for animals properly;	▪ Home Pet Study ▪ Hamsters as Pets
- describe how humans produce food by raising livestock;	▪ Honeybees ▪ Are these Foods?

Growth and Changes in Animals: Teacher Tips

What I Think I Know / What I Would Like to Know Activity

A great way to engage children in a new theme is to ask them what they think they know about a subject and what they would like to know about a subject. This activity can be completed as a whole group brainstorming session, in cooperative small groups or independently. Once children have had a chance to contemplate the theme, combine all information to create a class chart that can be hung up in the classroom. Throughout the study, periodically update the children's progress in accomplishing their goal of what they want to know and validate what they think they know.

Morning Messages

Morning messages provide students with interesting facts about the theme they are studying while also arranging teachable moments in the use of punctuation. Morning messages are an excellent way to get the learning going when the students enter in the morning. There are six morning messages included with this unit. The morning messages are in a letter format. There are several ways to present a morning message to your class:

Whole Group: Rewrite the morning message on a large sheet of chart paper and allow students to look for the "mistakes" in the letter. Then as a whole group read the letter together and use it as a springboard for a class discussion.

Individually: As children enter the classroom, give them a copy of the Morning Message and have them fix the "mistakes". The children practice reading the message with a friend until the class is ready to correct the morning message as a group. Use the Morning Message as a springboard for discussion.

Reading Cloze Activities

Cloze activities are not only useful for learning new information, but can be used to practise reading skills. Have children practise reading each cloze page individually or with a friend and finally with the teacher. Initial the page if reading is satisfactory.

Word List

Word lists create a theme related vocabulary. Place word lists on chart paper for students' reference during writing activities. Encourage students to add theme related words. In addition, classify the word list into the categories of nouns, verbs and adjectives.

Unit Assessment Strategies

Learning Inventory Test

At the completion of the unit, children participate in a paper/pencil learning inventory test to assess their knowledge of science concepts covered during the unit. The learning inventory includes multiple- choice questions, true and false, fill the blank, and some written answers.

Home Pet Study

Children take observations for three days of a home pet. The purpose of the project is to describe the life processes of an animal that they have observed and to demonstrate an awareness of ways of caring for animals properly.

Constructed Response- Learning Logs

Learning logs are an excellent means for children to organize their thoughts and ideas about the science concepts presented. Grammar, spelling or syntax should not be emphasized. The student responses give the teacher opportunities to plan follow up activities that may review and clarify concepts learned.

Learning log entries may be done on a daily basis or intermittently depending on scheduling. Entries should be brief. Time allotted for completion should be less than fifteen minutes. Entries can be done with a whole group, small group or an individual.

Learning logs can include the following kinds of entries:

- Direct instructions by the teacher;
- Key ideas;
- Personal reflections;
- Questions that arise;
- Connections discovered;
- Problem solving strategies;
- Labeled diagrams and pictures.

Learning logs can take the form of:

- Science journal;
- Entries in a classroom portfolio;
- Reflective page.

Student Centered Parent Conferences:

Children have an opportunity to share their portfolio work with their parents.

Student Self-Assessment:

Children will evaluate themselves in different areas such as group skills, oral presentation skills and to reflect on what they learned.

Culminating Activity: Creation of a Class Zoo

The class project is intended to incorporate the expectations under Developing Skills of Inquiry, Design and Communication. Children are asked to do the following challenge:

> You and your classmates have been asked by the world wildlife organization to create a unique place where all kinds of different animals may live. You need to think about the different habitats, and other environmental conditions to make your place a safe place for the animals.

The following pages include a six step format that encourages children to use the writing process. In this project children are asked to create a diorama depicting their chosen animal in it's habitat. Children should be encouraged to add as many details as possible to their diorama and to label objects. In addition, a written report should be included. Children may use this report as a reference during an oral presentation.

Other Teacher Tips:

➢ Arrange final products in the classroom according to type of animal or type of habitat;
➢ Create invitations and invite other classes and parents to share projects and celebrate the learning;
➢ Decorate the classroom with artwork to support the dioramas.

Culminating Activity: Creation of a Class Zoo
Planner Page

Step One: (pre-writing) Choosing Your Animal

The animal I would like to know more about is:

_____

My animal is a(n):   mammal   amphibian   insect   reptile

Gather different types of resources, like CD Roms, books, internet sites and videos.

Use the web planner to organize information.
These headings are a guide to organizing your work.

Each heading on your web planner should be a different colour.
    (*E.G. Food could be red, so all the information you find about what your animal eats, will be underlined in red!*)

Culminating Activity: Creation of a Class Zoo
Web Planner Page

Use this page to organize your Research Action Project.
Some headings to choose from: (You should choose at least four)

- ◆   **What and how it eats.**
- ◆   **Where it lives.**
- ◆   **What it looks like.**
- ◆   **Special features.**
- ◆   **Interesting facts.**

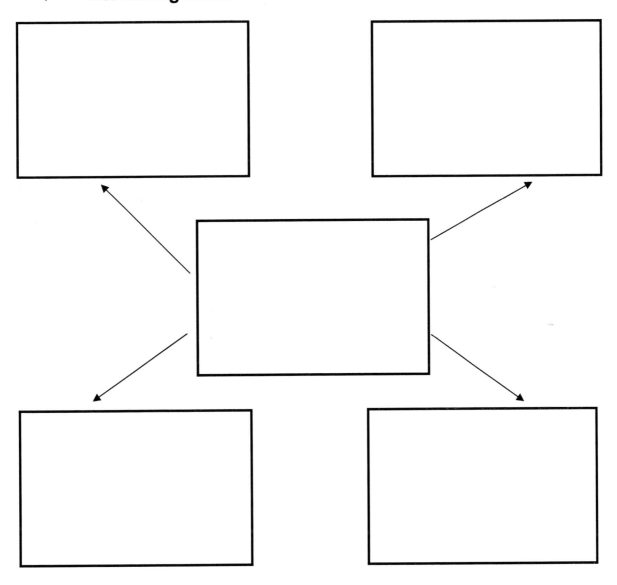

Culminating Activity: Creation of a Class Zoo

Step Two: (drafting) Gathering and Organizing Your Information

1. Using one resource at a time, read for information on your topic.

2. Using your information recording sheet, make jot notes in your own words.

3. Using a coloured pencil underline the information according to the colour you chose for your heading on your web.

   (*E.G. If you chose yellow to show all the information you found about habitat, all the places your animal lives will be underlined in yellow.*)

4. Re-write your information for each heading from the web, so all the information underlined in each colour is together, on a separate page.

Step Three: (revising) Making It Better!

In a small group or with a friend, read your draft for meaning and then add, delete, or change words to make your writing better.

Step Four: (editing) The Final Check

In a small group or with a friend, use this editing check-list to make sure you:
- ☐ used **capitals** at the beginning of sentences and for names and for your titles;
- ☐ have **periods** or questions or exclamation marks at the ends of sentences;
- ☐ used **commas** to separate series of words;
- ☐ **spelled** words correctly.

Culminating Activity: Creation of a Class Zoo

Resource title: _____

Type of resource: CD Rom   Book   Video   Other

Author of resource: _____

Where I found it: Library   Classroom   Home   Other

This resource was: O.K.   Good   Excellent

Jot Notes: _____

_____

_____

_____

_____

_____

_____

_____

_____

Culminating Activity: Creation of a Class Zoo

Step Five: (publishing) Putting It All Together!

1. Discuss with your teacher changes to be made to your work, or if you are ready for the next step.

2. Organize your information on a presentation board.

Think about:
➤ the size of your printing, making sure it is easy to read from far away;
➤ drawing detailed pictures to go with your information;
➤ making a model or diorama, etc. to go with your project.

Step Six: (presenting it) Telling About It

1. Using your presentation board, model or diorama, practice showing and talking about your Action Research Project:

➤ use your best voice, speaking slowly, and making sure it is loud so everyone can hear;
➤ look at your audience and try not to sway;
➤ introduce your project in an interesting way (Riddle, or Question);
➤ choose the most important things to tell. Use your web planner for ideas.;
➤ point to your pictures, model, or diorama, as you present;

Step Seven (reflection) Thinking About My Work

Conference with your teacher about how you worked and what you did well and what you would like to do better next time.

About Learning Centres

Learning centres provide optimal opportunities for children to practise interacting and sharing ideas with their peers in positive ways. Centre based learning encourages children to take ownership of their learning.

In order to run successful learning centres, good planning on the part of the teacher is essential. Follow these steps:

First: Examine your timetable and decide on one time block to be devoted consistently to learning centre time.

Second: Decide how many centres will be set up during learning centres and what they will be.

Third: Store what is needed for each activity in their individual bin. In this way, centres are organized and ready to go. Each centre bin should include:

- An activity card describing the activity;
- All materials needed to complete the activity for each child;
- Samples of completed work to show students.

Fourth: Introduce and explain the expectations of each learning centre to the class. This is the time to teach any specific skills needed to complete a centre. In addition review how many students are to work at each centre.

If a learning centre approach is new to your classroom, balance your centres so that some of the activities will need minimum teacher direction, such as a construction centre or art centre. This will:

- Allow students to learn routines in how to move through each centre;
- Control the number of children allowed at a centre;
- Encourage children to work independently and with others.

The teacher should circulate amongst the centres encouraging children:

- To be self-directed learners;
- To use their peers as a resource for help;
- To work to their fullest potential.

Sample Morning Messages

dear Entomologists;
Did you know OVer half of the world'S inSects live in the rainforests! There are More insectS there than iN any other part of the WorLd? Some have not Even been discovered yeT The rainForest is Moist and Warm, so some of these insects grow to HUGE sizes.

Think small!

Happy Investigating!

_____

Dear Herpetologists;
scientists who study Reptiles are Called, herpetologists, Did you know reptiles are cousins tO the dinOsaurs. Reptiles laY eggs, but they are not chickens. reptiles have scales, bones and they breaThe air   They are cold-blooded which meanS they are the same Temperature as the air around Them. There are four kinds of reptiles turtles lizards? Snakes and crocodilians.

Happy Investigating!

_____

Sample Morning Messages

Dear Reptile Researchers;
did you know tHat the word Tuatara means 'spiny'. Tuatara are strange looking reptiles that Look like lizards, but aren't? they are speCial because they have A Third eye on the top of their Head that is coVered by their skin. tuatara also have a spiny crest dOwn their Neck and Back In addition, tuatara are oNe Of the few rePtiles that can Making croaking noises?

Now you know!

_____

dear mammals;
Did you know thaT mammals have fur or hair on some Part of their boDies they give milk to their young and are warm blooded? mammals Breathe air in their lungs and have a baCkbone. Look at the Person next to you, they, are a mammal.

Have a great day!

_____

Dear mammals;
Did You know that Mammals caN be found in the Air, in the Water, on Land and on the trees. the largest mammal oN the earth is the Blue Whale and is About As long as a hockey rink The smallest mammal on the earTh is the Pygmy shrew and is as biG as the wiDth of a child's finger?

Happy learning!

_____

Growth and Changes in Animals: Parent Letter

Dear Parents and Guardians,

Your child will be investigating the captivating world of animals, mammals, reptiles, and insects. By the end of our study, your child should be able to:

- ✓ demonstrate an understanding of the similarities and differences among various types of animals and the ways in which animals adapt to different environmental conditions;
- ✓ investigate physical and behavioural characteristics and the process of growth of different types of animals;
- ✓ identify ways that humans affect other animals.

This study will be used as a springboard for numerous activities. In addition, children will be given the opportunity to complete an at home pet study. Look for the information package soon!

Families may contribute to our study by lending any resources, such as CD ROMS, books, newspaper articles, collections, tapes etc.

Your enthusiastic participation in our class study is greatly appreciated!

Sincerely,

mammal

reptile

insect

amphibian

Sight Vocabulary Cards

species

endangered

extinct

habitat

herbivore

carnivore

omnivore

hibernation

All About Mammals

Did you know that you are a mammal? Mammal babies are born alive and are the only creatures that drink their mother's milk. All mammals have fur or hair; are warm-blooded; have teeth and a backbone.

You cannot always tell a mammal by the way it looks. The fish shaped porpoise, the long necked giraffe, the enormous elephant and the winged bat all belong to the mammal family.

A hairy covering helps to keep mammals protected from the cold and the rain. Some mammals have a lot of hair and some don't. On some mammals such as the whale, there are only a few hairs around its mouth. Horses have a stiff covering of hair; sheep have curly wool, while people have hair on their heads.

Mammals are carnivores, herbivores or omnivores. Carnivores eat only meat using their canine teeth for tearing flesh. Grizzly bears and alligators are carnivores. Herbivores eat only plants using flat molars for grinding and crushing plant fibers. Moose and Panda bears are herbivores. Omnivores eat both, this is why humans have pointy and flat teeth. Everyone knows a lion eats meat and a cow eats grass, but did you know that a moose eats tree bark?

The biggest mammal is the blue whale and it is as big as thirty elephants. The tiniest mammal is the pygmy shrew and it is about the size of your finger.

GeoWat innovative teacher publishing inc. © 2002

Thinking about: All About Mammals

1. List four ways to identify a mammal:

_____   _____

_____   _____

2. Find the missing word from the reading:

A hairy covering helps to keep mammals _____ from

the cold and the _____. Some mammals have a lot of

_____ and some don't. On some mammals such as the

_____, there are only a few hairs around it's mouth.

_____ have a stiff covering of hair,

_____ have curly wool, while _____ have hair

on their heads.

3. Fill in the blank using information from the reading:

A. Carnivores eat meat using _____ teeth for tearing.

B. Herbivores eat plants using _____ _____ for
   grinding.

C. Humans have both _____ and _____ teeth.

Mammal Word Search

W	O	C	B	E	A	V	E	R	D	Q	W
H	E	K	A	N	G	A	R	O	O	R	T
A	Y	U	T	O	I	P	T	D	G	Z	G
L	B	F	G	H	R	N	I	O	K	L	O
E	T	E	O	F	A	N	G	L	N	M	H
D	L	J	A	H	F	H	E	P	B	K	D
F	E	U	P	R	F	I	R	H	O	N	N
M	J	E	Q	W	E	Y	N	I	V	S	U
A	L	Z	R	H	U	M	A	N	X	C	O
E	M	N	T	B	V	T	I	B	B	A	R
O	P	M	O	N	K	E	Y	T	Y	U	G
D	O	R	M	O	U	S	E	L	T	A	C

WHALE	BEAVER	TIGER
DEER	CAT	GIRAFFE
BEAR	DOG	MONKEY
BAT	ELEPHANT	RABBIT
KANGAROO	GROUNDHOG	DOLPHIN

GeoWat innovative teacher publishing inc. © 2002

All About Whales

Did you know whales are air-breathing mammals that live in the ocean? They come in small sizes, like the Beluga Whales that can grow to 3 to 5 metres, and in big sizes like the Blue Whales that can grow to 31 metres.

Whales are not fish. They cannot stay under the water all the time. Before diving, whales must breathe fresh air into their lungs. Sperm Whales dive to the bottom of the sea floor for their food. They have been known to hold their breath for one hour and fifteen minutes! Whales have special nostrils on the top of their heads called **blowholes**. When whales surface, they blow out their warm wet breath making a **spout**.

There are two types of whales. The first type of whale has teeth and is called toothed whales, or **Odontoceti**. Some toothed whales are the Narwhal Killer Whale and the Pilot Whale.

The second type of whale has no teeth. They have long fringed blades hanging from their upper jaws that look like big toothbrushes. These 'toothbrushes' are called **baleen**.

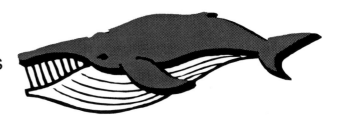

The baleen helps the whale **strain** out food from the water. Baleen whales are also known as **Mysticeti**. Some baleen whales are the Gray Whale, and the Blue Whale.

Thinking about: All About Whales

1. What kind of animals are whales?

_____

2. How do whales breathe?

_____

3. Name two types of whales.

_____

4. How do whales use baleen?

_____

5. Name two baleen whales.

_____

6. Name two toothed whales.

_____

grey whale

killer whale

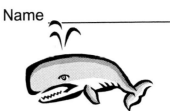

Thinking about: All About Whales

7. Match the word to the meaning in the reading.

blowhole	whales that don't have teeth
Odontoceti	long fringed blades, like a toothbrush
baleen	a whale's wet warm breath
Mysticeti	toothed whales
strain	special nostrils
spout	to filter

8. Match the word phrases to make sentences:

A. Whales are mammals	fresh air into their lungs.
B. Whales must breathe	they blow out warm wet breath.
C. When whales surface	that live in the ocean.

Hamsters As Pets

Did you know hamsters are part of the rodent family? Other rodents include rats, squirrels, and mice. Even Canada's symbol, the beaver, is a rodent! Rodents make up about half of the world's mammals. Rodents have babies very quickly and eat just about anything, and live almost everywhere.

Hamsters are the cute little pets we usually see in pet stores, but they can live in the wild too! In the wild, hamsters store as much as one whole garbage bag of potatoes or grain in their burrows or homes!

Pet hamsters need special care. A hamster needs a clean cage with lots of room. It also needs good food to eat, like fruit, vegetables, seeds and tiny bits of raw meat. Hamsters should have clean water, too.

Hamsters like to play, and run around their cage. A wheel and tubes are the hamster's playground. They like to tear up paper too!

You may love to handle your hamster, but be careful hamsters may bite if they are tired when you play with them.

GeoWat innovative teacher publishing inc. © 2002

Thinking about: Hamsters As Pets

1. Name two animals that are rodents.

_____

2. Where can hamsters live?

_____

3. What do hamsters like to do in their cages?

_____

4. When do you need to be careful with a hamster?

_____

5. How is having a pet hamster different from having another kind of pet like a cat, dog or fish? How is it the same?

_____

_____

_____

_____

_____

_____

Thinking about: Hamsters As Pets

6. Find the missing word from the reading.

A. Pet _____ need special care.

B. A hamster needs a clean _____ with lots of room.

C. It also needs good food to eat, like_____,

vegetables, _____and tiny bits of _____meat.

7. List some important ways to look after a pet hamster:

A._____

B._____

C._____

D._____

E._____

8. Would you want to have a pet hamster? Explain

_____

_____

_____

Grizzly Bears

Did you know grizzly bears are huge mammals? They live mostly in British Columbia and the Yukon Territory. When walking on all four feet, they can be as tall as a small child and as long a car. When a grizzly bear stands up, it is taller than the top of a door! Most animals are afraid of grizzly bears.

A mother grizzly bear finds a den to sleep in for the winter as the weather gets cold. In the middle of winter her babies are born. Baby grizzly bears are called cubs. The cubs are very small and need their mother to take care of them.

Grizzly bear cubs are two months old before they can walk. By spring, cubs can follow their mother out of the den and spend the summer running with her. When the cold weather comes, the cubs go back into the den for the winter.

When the next spring comes, the cubs follow their mother out of the den. It is not long before the mother bear knows that the cubs are ready to take care of themselves and chases them away.

It takes a cub about ten years to become a full-grown grizzly bear. Grizzly bears spend their days feeding on salmon from mountain streams or hunting small animals for food. They like meat best, but will eat berries and roots. Did you know that grizzly bears have claws on their front paws that grow as long as a ruler?

Name _____

Thinking about: Grizzly Bears

1. Where do grizzly bears live?

_____

2. What are baby grizzly bears called?

_____

3. How old are grizzly cubs before they can walk?

_____

4. Where do grizzly cubs go when the weather gets colder?

_____

5. How long does it take a grizzly cub to become full grown?

_____

6. Name something a grizzly bear likes to eat.

_____

Thinking about: Grizzly Bears

7. Match the word phrases to make sentences:

A. Grizzly bears are   during the winter.

B. Grizzly bears live in   den to sleep in for the
                                                winter.

C. Grizzly cubs are born   salmon, berries and
                                                roots.

D. A mother grizzly bear finds a   for a grizzly bear to
                                                become full grown.

E. It takes about ten years   huge mammals.

F. Grizzly bears eat   British Columbia and
                                                the Yukon Territory.

8. Think about it!

What surprising things did you learn about grizzlies from the reading?

_____

_____

_____

Name _____

Incredible Insects

Did you the world is full of insects? Insects outnumber any other living group in the world!

Insects live everywhere. Insects can be found from the hot tropical forests to the ice cold polar regions. Their tiny size helps the insect live in these amazing places. Insects can easily hide from enemies, and they do not need a lot of food to survive.

Insects wear their skeleton outside their body. A hard shell supports them instead of a backbone. Their antennae act like noses and hands helping them to smell and feel.

All insects have three parts to their body, the head, the thorax, and the abdomen. Most insects change as they grow older. They go through life cycle stages, or metamorphosis. Egg, larva, pupa, and adult are the most common.

Some people think the world would be more peaceful without insects. No mosquitoes to buzz in our ears. No houseflies to pester us. No ants to invade our picnics.

Without insects, there would be no apples to eat, because bees did not pollinate the trees. There would be no fireflies to brighten up a summer's night. There would be no songbirds to sing, because they need bugs to eat for their meals. There would be no frogs or fish or other insect-eating creatures. What a sad world we would have without insects!

Name _____

Thinking about: Incredible Insects

1. Name two places where insects can be found.

_____

2. What do insects have instead of a backbone?

_____

3. What are an insect's antennae used for?

_____

4. Name the four life cycle stages of an insect.

_____, _____, _____, _____

5. Label the parts of the insect:

thorax   head   abdomen   antennae   legs

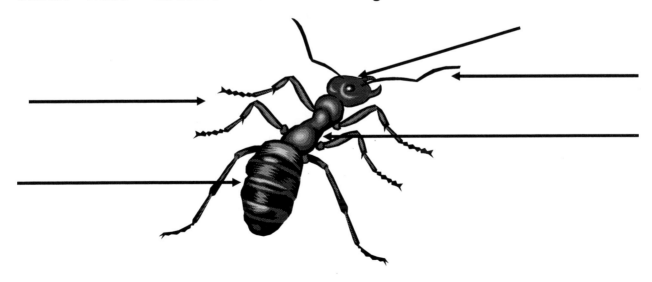

GeoWat innovative teacher publishing inc. © 2002

33

Life Cycle of a Monarch Butterfly

Did you know in the fall Monarch butterflies can be seen many places in Canada? Their bright orange and black wings make them easily recognized. The butterfly lays its eggs on a leaf. The tiny caterpillars hatch and eat to get bigger. When the caterpillars are bigger, and ready, they make a chrysalis that hangs from a branch or leaf.   Inside the chrysalis, the caterpillar goes through a metamorphosis or change. A butterfly pushes its way out of the chrysalis and starts the life cycle over again.

Life Cycle of a Monarch Butterfly

Draw the pictures to match the statements. Cut out the boxes with their statements and paste them in order on a separate paper.

A caterpillar makes a chrysalis and it hangs from a branch.

A caterpillar hatches and begins to eat leaves.

The butterfly lays its egg on a leaf.

A butterfly pushes its way out of the chrysalis.

Honeybees

Did you know **honeybees** have been making honey for millions of years? Some beekeepers keep honeybees as a hobby, while others farm honey for a living. People use **honey** for food, medicine and beauty products. To produce 2.2 kilograms of honey a bee must travel the same distance as three orbits around the earth.   In Canada,we make about 220 million kilograms of honey each year. That's a lot of sweet gooey honey for you and me!

Did you know honeybees cannot live alone?   They live in a **colony** as a community where they depend on each other. Each bee has a job to do. The **queen** is the mother of all the bees in the **hive**.   She is waited on, protected and fed by the worker bees. The queen only has one job, and that is to lay eggs that grow into adults. She can lay as many as 2000 eggs in a day! Imagine how many eggs she lays in her three-year life.

Drones are lazy. They don't work in the hive, but they do have a job. Their job is to mate with the queen. The queen only mates once in her lifetime, so when the hive gets too full, the drones are forced to leave.

The tiny **worker bees** are females. They have many jobs like feeding the baby larva, cleaning the cone, making honey, storing pollen, taking care of the queen and guarding the hive. Even then their job is not finished. The last job a worker bee does is to become a **field bee** that collects pollen, **nectar** and water to feed the colony. They work so hard, their wings wear out and they usually die in the field.

Thinking about: Honeybees

1. How do people use honey?

_____

2. What is the distance a honeybee must travel to produce 2.2 kilograms of honey?

_____

_____

3. If you could be a honeybee in a hive, what job would you want to have and why?

_____

_____

4. Why is the life of a worker bee hard?

_____

_____

Thinking about: Honeybees:

5. Match the meaning of each word in the reading:

A. Colony

B. Drone

C. Field Bee

D. Hive

E. Honey

F. Honeybee

G. Nectar

H. Queen

I. Worker bee

sweet liquid produced by bees

collected by bees from flowers

a community of bees

the mother of all bees

male honeybee

a worker that gathers pollen, nectar or water

the place where honeybees live

a bee that does many jobs

a bee that makes honey

GeoWat innovative teacher publishing inc. © 2002

All About Reptiles

Did you know reptiles are incredible animals? There are reptiles with shells on their backs, like turtles. There are reptiles with four legs that live on land, like lizards. There are reptiles with four legs that live in the water, like crocodiles. There are reptiles that have no legs, like snakes. There are even reptiles that have a third "eye", like the tuatara!

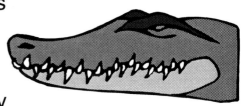

All reptiles have backbones in their bodies. Usually they have dry skin covered with scales and claws on their feet. Reptiles are cold-blooded. This means their bodies are no warmer than the air around them. On cold days reptiles move slowly without much energy. They don't have to make heat like a warm-blooded animal does, so they don't have to eat as much as a warm-blooded animal. Did you know some reptiles go for more than a year without eating?

Baby reptiles are hatched from eggs. Some mothers carry their eggs inside their bodies until they hatch, but most reptiles lay their eggs in a warm place.

Usually baby reptiles learn to take care of themselves without help from their moms. When they hatch from their eggs, they are ready to face the world on their own. Several times a year a reptile sheds it's skin depending on how quickly it grows. Often reptiles will eat their skin because it is full of protein. Some reptiles can change colours to match their surroundings, like the chameleon.

Thinking about: All About Reptiles

1. Name four types of reptiles:

_____

_____

_____

_____

2. Find the missing words from the reading:

A. Usually baby _____ learn to take care of themselves

without help from their _____.

B. When they hatch from their _____, they are ready to

face the world on their own.

C. Several times a year a reptile _____ it's

skin depending on how quickly it _____.

D. Often reptiles will eat their_____ because it is

full of _____.

E. Some reptiles can _____colours to match their

surroundings, like the _____.

Thinking about: All About Reptiles

3. Circle the right answer:

A. Reptiles have slimy skin.   Yes   No

B. Reptiles move slowly on cold days.   Yes   No

C. Baby reptiles are born alive.   Yes   No

D. Reptiles are warm-blooded.   Yes   No

E. All reptiles have three eyes.   Yes   No

F. Reptiles shed their skin.   Yes   No

4. Compare warm-blooded animals to cold-blooded animals:

A. How are they alike?

_____

B. How are they different?

_____

Reptile and Amphibian Word Search

A	H	B	G	A	F	G	L	H	C	S	H
C	L	K	O	S	Y	G	H	N	R	A	O
H	G	L	V	X	T	R	Z	U	O	L	R
A	O	J	I	I	T	H	G	F	C	A	N
M	R	Y	T	G	A	U	S	D	O	M	E
E	F	B	P	U	A	Q	R	J	D	A	D
L	E	A	S	A	F	T	H	T	I	N	T
E	E	D	F	N	H	C	O	V	L	D	O
O	R	D	U	A	K	L	L	R	E	E	A
N	T	O	R	T	O	I	S	E	Q	R	D
R	A	T	T	L	E	S	N	A	K	E	Z
Z	A	N	O	L	E	Q	G	E	C	K	O

RATTLE SNAKE   CROCODILE
HORNED TOAD   TORTOISE
GECKO   BOX TURTLE
IGUANA   ANOLE
CHAMELEON   ALLIGATOR
TREE FROG   SALAMANDER

Tree frog

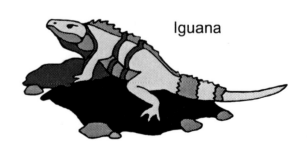

Iguana

Alligator Babies

Alligators come from eggs. They are reptiles. A female alligator lays up to 70 eggs in a hole and covers them up with leaves and mud. It takes two months for the eggs to hatch. The mother alligator's job is to keep the eggs safe from other animals. Tiny croaks from inside the nest are the signal that the babies are ready to hatch. The mother alligator helps to dig them out.

When all the baby alligators hatch, the mother alligator takes them to a safe place near the water. She carries them either in her mouth, or on her head. The baby alligators stay with their mother for one year.

Many baby alligators are in danger of being eaten by fish, birds or even other alligators. If they need help, their mother will protect them. It is a good thing baby alligators grow fast. They can get as long as a minivan. Alligators eat fish, snakes, small birds and turtles.

Since alligators are cold blooded, they enjoy lying in the sun on muddy riverbanks. Heat from the sun allows them to stay underwater. Since the alligator's eyes and nostrils are on the top of their heads, alligators can still see and breathe even though the rest of their body is underwater. They can stay underwater for hours!

Thinking about: Alligator Babies

1. What do alligators eat?

_____

2. Why does a mother alligator need to protect her babies?

_____

3. How does a mother alligator carry her babies to the water

_____

4. How do alligators spend their days? Why?

_____

_____

Thinking about: Alligator Babies:

5. Circle the right answer:

A. Alligators are born alive.	Yes	No
B. Alligators can stay underwater for hours.	Yes	No
C. Baby alligators take a long time to grow.	Yes	No
D. Alligators are warm blooded.	Yes	No
E. A mother alligator listens for croaks from her nest.	Yes	No
F. Baby alligators don't need their mother.	Yes	No
G. Heat from the sun warms an alligator.	Yes	No
H. An alligator's nest is made from wet leaves and mud.	Yes	No
I. An alligator is longer than a minivan.	Yes	No
J. A female alligator can lay up to 70 eggs.	Yes	No

Reptiles: The King Cobra

Did you know snakes are the only animals that are missing parts of their body like legs, eyelids, claws and outside ear openings?

No matter how scary you think snakes are, the King Cobra is a special reptile. They have bodies that twist, slither, coil and climb. Their senses are very well developed. They smell by flicking their tongue in and out.

The King Cobra can be as long as a pick-up truck and its head is the size of a grown man's fist. You can tell if a snake is a King Cobra by the hood around its head. It makes this hood by flattening out the bones around its neck.

The King Cobra protects itself with small fangs at the front of its mouth that are used to bite its enemies. Inside the fangs of a King Cobra is a deadly poison called venom. The venom can kill in twenty minutes. This helps the King Cobra kill its prey. Then the King Cobra devours dinner by opening up its hinged mouth wide and swallowing the prey whole. Special mouth hinges lets a King Cobra eat things bigger than its head. Imagine if you could swallow a watermelon! Because the King Cobra is cold-blooded it only needs to eat a couple of times a year.

When a King Cobra is ready to lay eggs it builds a nest out of leaves, grass and soil. It coils itself around the nest until the eggs hatch. When the baby King Cobras hatch they are left to take care of themselves.

Thinking About Reptiles: The King Cobra

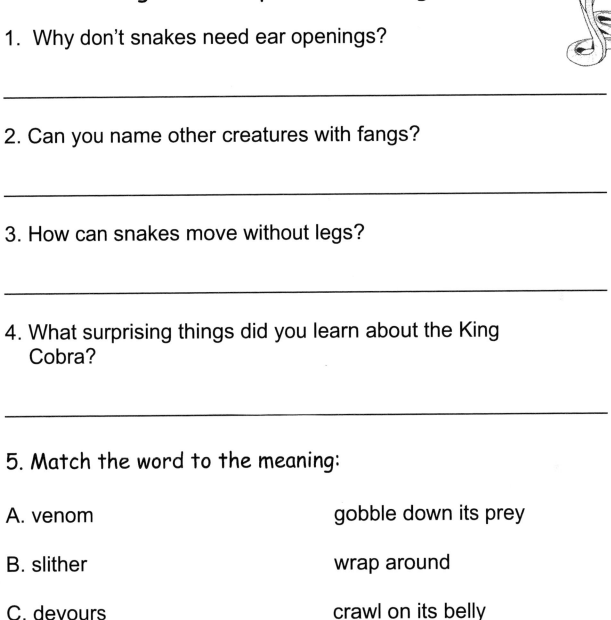

1. Why don't snakes need ear openings?

_____

2. Can you name other creatures with fangs?

_____

3. How can snakes move without legs?

_____

4. What surprising things did you learn about the King Cobra?

_____

5. Match the word to the meaning:

A. venom   gobble down its prey

B. slither   wrap around

C. devours   crawl on its belly

D. coil   a deadly poison

Name _____

Thinking About Reptiles: The King Cobra

6. Find the missing word from the reading.:

A. No matter how_____ you think snakes are, the

   King Cobra is a special _____.

B. Did you know snakes are the only _____ that

   are missing parts of their _____?

C. They are missing legs, _____, claws and outside ear

   _____.

D. They have bodies that twist,_____, coil and climb.

E. Their _____ are very well developed.

F. They smell by _____ their tongue in and out.

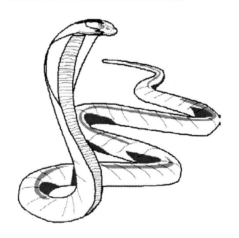

All About Amphibians

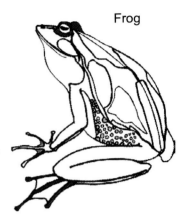
Frog

Did you know amphibians have smooth moist skin, are **cold-blooded** and lay eggs with soft shells? **Amphibians** can live on land and in the water. Some amphibians that you might know are frogs, toads and salamanders. Good places to look for amphibians include ponds, streams, and wetlands.

Most people think snakes and other reptiles are slimy, but really it is the amphibian that makes slime! The **slime** comes from glands in its skin. The slime helps keep the amphibian moist. Amphibians can also make their own poison. Some of the poisons just taste bad to an amphibian's enemy, while some of the poisons can be strong enough to kill them. If you see a brightly coloured amphibian, like the poisoned dart frog stay away! It is most likely poisonous.

Amphibians protect themselves by using colour to **camouflage**. Just like other animals, many amphibians blend into where they live. Have you ever noticed how frogs are often green like the ponds in which they live?

Most amphibians go through life cycle changes or a **metamorphosis**. Almost all amphibians start out as a plant-eating animal that lives in water. As adults they end up being meat-eating animals that live on both land and water.

GeoWat innovative teacher publishing inc. © 2002

Name _____

Thinking about: Amphibians

1. What are three characteristics of all amphibians?

_____

2. What are the names of three amphibians?

_____

3. Where are good places to look for amphibians?

_____

4. How do amphibians use slime?

_____

5. How can you tell an amphibian is poisonous?

_____

6. Name a way amphibians protect themselves. Tell what it means.

_____

Name _____

Thinking about: Amphibians

7. Using the reading, tell the meaning of these words.

A. amphibians

helps keep the amphibian moist

B. slime

go through life cycle changes

C. camouflage

can live on land and in the water

D. cold-blooded

blend into where they live

E. metamorphosis

their bodies are no warmer than the air around them

Life Cycle Of A Frog

Have you ever seen a mass of jelly floating by the edge of a pond? Maybe a frog had visited earlier and laid its eggs. You can tell a frog from a toad, because a frog's skin is smooth. To find out about the life cycle of a frog, follow these steps:

1. Colour the pictures on this page and cut them out.
2. Match the pictures to the statements on the next page.
3. This is the life cycle of a frog.

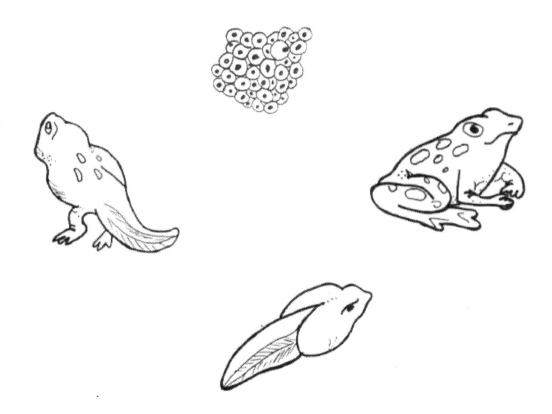

GeoWat innovative teacher publishing inc. © 2002

Name _____

Life Cycle Of A Frog

Match the pictures with the statements.

A frog lays eggs in a mass of jelly by the edge of a pond.

The eggs hatch and a tadpole swims into the pond.

The tadpole begins to grow legs and change its shape.

The tadpole completes its metamorphosis or change and becomes a frog.

GeoWat innovative teacher publishing inc. © 2002

Animal Life Cycles

Did you know a skunk and a dog have some things in common? They both have the same life cycle. They are both born alive and they look just like their parents. They are both helpless as babies, and need their mom for food and protection. Skunks and dogs drink their mothers' milk and grow quickly. They learn from their mothers to take care of themselves.

What does a butterfly and frog have in common? They both have similar life cycles. They are both born from eggs and go through many changes until they become an adult. When butterflies and frogs are hatched, they look different from the adults. They even have different names. Butterflies begin their life cycle as caterpillars and frogs begin their life cycle as tadpoles. Caterpillars and tadpoles have to take care of themselves as soon as they are born.

Fill in the blank using information from the reading:

1. _____ and _____ learn from their mothers to take care of themselves.

2. Both the _____ and the _____ are born from eggs and go through many changes until they become an adult.

3. _____ and _____ have to take care of themselves as soon as they are born.

Thinking about: Animal Life Cycles

Using the information from the story fill in the chart below:

Think about how the life cycles of these animals are alike or different. Mark the chart with an "X".	Skunk	Dog	Frog	Butterfly
Babies are hatched from eggs.				
Mothers feed their babies milk.				
Babies take care of themselves.				
Babies look different from the adult.				
Babies are born alive.				
Babies look like the adult.				
Babies go through many life cycle changes.				
Mothers protect their babies.				

What do you notice from the information in the chart?

_____

_____

Name _____

What Will I Look Like When I Grow Up?

When animals are born, sometimes they look just like their parents. Some animals change just a little, while other animals change a lot as they grow up. Look at the animals below. Match the baby animal to the adult animal.

Endangered Species

Did you know there are some animals that have lived on Earth that are not alive anymore? We say these animals are extinct. The dinosaurs are a good example of extinct creatures.

Animals become extinct for many reasons. Sometimes they are hunted for food, or for fur, or parts of their bodies like tusks or horns. Sometimes they are hunted for things that can be made from their body parts, or to be put in zoos, or for pets. Sometimes people think they are dangerous animals like the wolf, and they try to kill them.

Habitats are the best or natural place for an animal to live. Often, people building houses or roads chase animals out of their habitats. Land is cleared, forests are cut down, and swamps are drained. The animals lose their food and homes.

Did you know pollution also kills many animals? For example, when poisons are sprayed on crops to kill insects, the birds that eat the insects are poisoned too. Sometimes the poison seeps into the ground and the water supply becomes poisoned.

Humans are helping to protect animals by setting up special zoos where endangered animals are bred. This helps increase their numbers. People are also setting aside land to make sure animals like the Komodo dragon, and the desert tortoise have a safe place to live and grow. These places are called habitat reserves.

Thinking about: Endangered Species

Match the word to the meaning in this story:

dangerous	the best place for an animal to live
extinct	land to keep animals safe
reserve	at risk of disappearing
protect	harmful, dirty material in land, air or water
endangered	to produce more animals
pollution	animals that are no longer alive
zoo	a group of animals that are similar
species	a place where people can see wild animals on display
habitat	not safe, harmful
bred (breed)	to keep something safe

Thinking about: Endangered Species

1. Name two reasons why animals become extinct:

_____

_____

2. How does pollution kill many animals?

_____

3. What is a wild life reserve?

_____

4. Do you think a wild life reserve is helpful? Why?

_____

_____

5. Why do we need to take care of animals?

_____

_____

Name _____

Migration, Hibernation and Dormancy

Did you know most birds like the robin fly south for the winter? This is because the food they eat is gone. Insects die or burrow themselves under tree bark. Berries and seeds are no longer available, so the birds fly where food is plentiful. Some insects, like the monarch butterfly, fly south too!

Whales swim to warmer water, and salmon go back to their home to have their babies. Migration is when animals find warmer regions during cold weather. Some birds like the Canada Goose fly south for the winter. No one is sure how the birds find their way south for winter and back in the fall. Some scientists think the birds use the sun, the moon and the stars to guide them. Others believe the birds sense the Earth's magnetic field.

Have you ever heard that bears sleep all winter long? This is called hibernation. During hibernation, an animal's body temperature sinks to match the weather outside. Its blood pressure drops and its heartbeat slows down. The animal lives off the fat it has stored in its body over the warmer months. Little animals like the dormouse, and some adult insects, go into a deeper sleep called dormancy.

The difference between dormancy and hibernation is the depth of the sleep. Bears can wake up for short periods, but the dormouse will stay sleeping, even if he were picked up in your hand! Do not try this with a bear!

Thinking about: Migration, Hibernation and Dormancy

1. Match the definition:

A. Migration

a deeper sleep than hibernation.

B. Hibernation

moving from one place to another.

C. Dormancy

sleeping all winter long.

2. Tell what each of these animals does:

Migrate   **Hibernate**   **Dormant**

Whale _____   Robin _____

Bear _____   Monarch Butterfly _____

Salmon _____   Dormouse _____

How Animals Change With The Seasons

Have you ever noticed how your cat or dog sheds its fur in the spring and fall? It is trying to get ready for the seasonal change. In the summer, the dog or cat needs a lighter coat to help keep it cool. In the winter, it needs a warmer coat to help keep it warm. Therefore, it gets rid of its fur and grows new fur just before the season.

Other mammals do similar things to get ready for the change in the season. The bear eats a lot during the fall in order to store fat for the long sleep it will take during the winter. Beavers collect branches and store them near the entrance to their lodges, or homes. This will be their supply of winter food. Squirrels are busy during the summer months collecting and storing seeds and grains for their winter meals.

How do humans get ready for winter? Make a list of some of the things you or your family might do.

_____

_____

_____

The Canada Goose

Did you know the Canada goose belongs to the family known as waterfowl? All waterfowl have webbed feet. Canada geese have short legs, and tails and long strong necks and wings. They have a black head with a wide white band across their throat and cheeks. They fly in "V" **formations** and migrate south in the fall. Canada geese choose one mate for life, and even if something happens to that mate, they will not choose a new partner.

Waterfowl build their nests on the ground to lay their eggs. They lose their flight feathers soon after the eggs hatch, and for a short time, they cannot fly, until the feathers grow back. If their nests were in trees, they would be unable to care for their young.

The Canada goose has beautiful feathers covering its back. These feathers are kept water resistant by "preening". **Preening** is when the bird collects oil from a gland under its tail, and spreads it over its feathers. This keeps the feathers **water-proof**. Under these outer feathers the goose grows down. Down feathers, do not have a hard shaft through the middle like the outer feathers. These soft down feathers keep the goose warm. People like to get the down feathers and fill coats and sleeping bags with them. They trap warm air next to the body and keep people warm too!

Along the edge of the Canada goose's wings are long strong **flight feathers**. These feathers help the goose fly about 60 kilometres an hour. They also help the goose fly long distances when it migrates.

The Canada Goose

1. Using the reading, tell the meaning of these words.

A. **formations**   when a bird spreads oil on its feathers.

B. **waterfowl**   water cannot go through.

C. **preening**   flying south for the winter.

D. **water-proof**   a special shape.

E. **flight feathers**   birds with webbed feet who build nests on the ground.

F. **migration**   strong feathers on a bird's wing.

2. Use the reading to help you find the missing words.

A. Down _____ do not have a hard

_____ through the middle like the outer feathers.

B. These soft_____ feathers keep

the goose warm.

Name _____

The Moose

Did you know moose are the largest member of the deer family? They are found everywhere in Canadian forests, and their picture can be found on the back of a quarter.

A bull or male moose can weigh as much as six wrestlers, and stand taller than most men! That means a kindergarten child would be up to the bull moose's knee! Only bull moose have antlers. Females, or cows are smaller than bulls but they still can be as big as a large horse!

The bull has huge antlers, but the male moose does not start his life with antlers. After starting as tiny brown buttons, the antlers slowly grow a bit bigger each year, until they form on each side of his head. This takes about seven years.

The moose's legs are long and lean. He looks like he is walking on stilts! These long skinny legs allow the moose to stride through the bush and over fallen logs. They also help him wade through deep snow and reach tall trees for food. Long legs are good for defending yourself too! The moose kicks out his legs at attacking wolves or runs swiftly through the woods to escape.

The moose has very poor eyesight even though his large brown eyes seem to see everything! Lucky for the moose, his ears are big and can catch sound waves easily. They can hear much better than we can!

The moose is an herbivore and he loves to nibble juicy leaves, twigs and plants. The moose loves to swim. His favourite treat is water lilies!

The Moose

Fill in the correct bubble.

1. Moose are members of the

   - ○   deer family
   - ○   polar bear family
   - ○   your family
   - ○   none of the above

2. Bull moose means

   - ○   female moose
   - ○   girl moose
   - ○   good moose
   - ○   male moose

3. Moose have

   - ○   sharp eyesight and small ears
   - ○   short legs and antlers
   - ○   long legs and antlers
   - ○   wings and feathers

4. Moose like to eat

   - ○   water lilies
   - ○   leaves
   - ○   twigs
   - ○   all of the above

The Moose

5. Using information from the reading, fill
   in the chart below.

What they eat	
What they look like.	
Where they live.	
Where you can find their picture.	

Name _____

Are these foods?

Did you know pigs, chickens, turkey and cattle are types of livestock that provide us with food? Cows give us milk to drink and to make into butter, cheese and ice cream. Chickens give us meat, and eggs. Pigs give us bacon and ham. To some people, these would be strange and unusual foods.

Have you ever tried turtle soup, frog's legs, rattlesnake steaks, alligator nuggets, snails, or baked tarantula? In many parts of the world, people have enjoyed eating creatures like these for a very long time. Meat from lizards, snakes and turtles has become so popular that many were captured and sold each year. People began to worry that over hunting these creatures would endanger, or harm them. Now we have unusual farms to grow these animals for our dinner tables.

Survey a group of friends
Find out what they would like to taste.

Turtle Soup	Snake Steak	Frog's Legs	Baked Tarantula	Alligator Nuggets	Lizard	Garlic Snails

What was the most popular choice? _____

Name _____

Home Pet Study: Parent Letter

Parents have an important role to play in supporting their child's learning. For our class study of Life Systems: Growth and Changes in Animals your child has the opportunity to complete a home study project. This study of a home pet is designed to relate science to the outside world. The student is expected to show understanding of connections of science in both familiar and unfamiliar contexts.

The student has the option of using a pet found at home, at school, in a pet store, at a neighbour's, or belonging to another family member.

The following curriculum outcomes will be covered in the home project:

♦   describe features of the environment that support the growth of familiar animals;
♦   demonstrate an understanding of the requirements of small animals for survival;
♦   describe the life processes of an animal that they have observed;
♦   demonstrate awareness of ways of caring for animals properly.

Please assist your child in gathering and organizing information.

Enjoy!

_____

Home Pet Study

This is a portrait of my pet and where it lives.

Name _____

Watch your pet for three days. Record behaviour patterns on the chart below.

Home Pet Study Day _____

MORNING	OBSERVATIONS:
eats:	
rests:	
plays:	

AFTERNOON	OBSERVATIONS:
eats:	
rests:	
plays:	

NIGHT	OBSERVATIONS:
eats:	
rests:	
plays:	

The thing that surprised me about my pet was...

After watching my pet for three days, this is what I discovered:

In order to care for my pet properly I need to...

_____

_____

_____

_____

My pet doesn't like it when I ...

_____

_____

_____

_____

The best thing about my pet is...

_____

Name _____

Growth and Changes in Animals: Assessment

Basic Concepts	Letter Grade	Lessons Completed
- identify and describe the major physical characteristics of different types of animals;		➢ Mammals ➢ Reptiles ➢ Amphibians ➢ Insects
- identify and describe behavioural characteristics that enable animals to survive;		➢ Migration, Hibernation and Dormancy
- classify a variety of animals using observable characteristics;		➢ Whales ➢ King Cobra
- compare ways in which animals eat their food, move and use their environment to meet their needs;		➢ All About _____
- describe changes in the appearance and activity of an animal as it goes through its complete life cycle;		➢ Life Cycle of a Frog ➢ Life Cycle of a Monarch Butterfly
- compare the life cycles of some animals that have similar life cycles and some that have different life cycles;		➢ Comparing Animal Life Cycles
- identify constant traits and changing traits in animals as they grow and compare the appearance of young and mature animals of the same species;		➢ Growing Up
- describe ways in which animals respond and adapt to their environment;		➢ How Animals Change With The Seasons
- compare ways in which different animals care for their young;		➢ Grizzly Bears ➢ Alligator Babies

Teacher Comments:

_____

_____

_____

_____

_____

_____

Growth and Changes in Animals: Assessment

Relating Science and Technology to the World Outside the School	Letter Grade	Lessons Completed
- describe features of the environment that support the growth of familiar animals;		➤ Home Pet Study
- identify and compare the effects of the seasons on animals;		➤ How Animals Change With The Seasons
- describe ways in which humans can help or harm other living things;		➤ Endangered Species
- demonstrate an understanding of the requirements of small animals for survival;		➤ Home Pet Study
- describe the life processes of an animal that they have observed;		➤ Home Pet Study
- demonstrate an awareness of ways of caring for animals properly;		➤ Home Pet Study ➤ Hamsters as Pets
- describe how humans produce food by raising livestock;		➤ Honeybees ➤ Are these Foods?

Teacher Comments:

_____

_____

_____

_____

_____

_____

_____

_____

Culminating Activity: Creation of Class Zoo- Animal

Written Report	Letter Grade	Comments
✓ diorama has a background ✓ labeled ✓ details of habitat included ✓ neat and colourful		
Written Report	**Letter Grade**	**Comments**
✓ uses appropriate vocabulary in describing their investigations. ✓ information is correct ✓ includes criteria ✓ correct Spelling and Punctution ✓ printing is neat and legible		
Oral Presentation	**Letter Grade**	**Comments**
✓ speaks in a clear voice ✓ introduces project in an interesting way ✓ well rehearsed ✓ communicates knowledge about the topic clearly		

Teacher Comments:

_____

_____

_____

_____

_____

_____

_____

_____

Name _____

Growth and Changes in Animals

Student Self- Evaluation: What I did in the Unit:

The best part of the unit was......

_____

I learned about........

_____

I want to learn more about....

_____

My Work Habits:	Yes	Sometimes	I need to try harder.
I listened to the teacher			
I tried my best to work on my own			
I did neat work with lots of details			
I was a good group member			

Rubric for Student Self-Assessment

A	**WOW**	✓ I completed my work independently on time and with care. ✓ I added details and followed the instructions without help. ✓ I understand and can talk about what I learned.
B	**BRAVO**	✓ I completed my work on time and with care. ✓ I followed the instructions with almost no help. ✓ I understand and can talk about what I learned.
C	**OKAY**	✓ I completed my work. ✓ I followed the instructions with some help. ✓ I understand and can talk about most of what I learned.
D	**UH-OH**	✓ I need to complete my work on time and with care. ✓ I should ask for help when I need it. ✓ I understand and can talk about a few of the things that I have learned.

Post the above rubric in your classroom to assist children in self- evaluation and direction for improvement in completing the tasks assigned.

Name _____

Learning Inventory Test:
Growth and Changes in Animals

1. Circle the Answer True or False

A. Mammals are warm- blooded.   True   False

B. Reptiles are warm-blooded.   True   False

C. Whales are reptiles.   True   False

D. Insects are only found in the rainforest.   True   False

E. All reptiles have backbones.   True   False

F. Reptiles move slowly on cold days.   True   False

G. Amphibians can make their own slime.   True   False

2. List three important ways to look after a pet at home:

A. _____

B. _____

C. _____

Learning Inventory Test:
Growth and Changes in Animals

3. Name two baby animals that need their mother to survive.

_____   _____

4. Name two baby animals that don't need their mother to survive.

_____   _____

5. How does camouflage help an animal protect it's self?

_____

_____

_____

6. Draw the life cycle of an animal you know:

Name of animal _____

GeoWat innovative teacher publishing inc. 2002©

Learning Inventory:
Growth and Changes in Animals

7. Multiple Choice: circle the right answer

Hibernation means:

A. changes colour
B. sleeps for a long time
C. flies south for the winter
D. none of the above

Migration means:

A. flies south for the winter
B. changes colour
C. sleeps for a long time
D. none of the above

Congratulations!

You are an animal expert!